D1592287

50+*Easy* Classical *Solos* for Clarinet

Wise Publications
London/New York/Paris/Sydney/Copenhagen/Madrid

Exclusive Distributors:
Music Sales Limited
8/9 Frith Street,
London W1V 5TZ, England.
Music Sales Pty Limited
120 Rothschild Avenue,
Rosebery, NSW 2018,
Australia.
Music Sales Corporation
257 Park Avenue South,
New York,
NY10010,
United States of America.

Order No. AM932052
ISBN 0-7119-5187-X
This book © Copyright 1995 by Wise Publications

Cover design by Pearce Marchbank, Studio Twenty
Quarked by Ben May

Printed in the United Kingdom by
Caligraving Limited, Thetford, Norfolk.

Your Guarantee of Quality
As publishers, we strive to produce every book
to the highest commercial standards.
This book has been carefully designed to minimise awkward
page turns and to make playing from it a real pleasure.
Particular care has been given to specifying acid-free,
neutral-sized paper made from pulps which have
not been elemental chlorine bleached. This pulp is
from farmed sustainable forests and was produced
with special regard for the environment.
Throughout, the printing and binding have been
planned to ensure a sturdy, attractive publication
which should give years of enjoyment.
If your copy fails to meet our high standards,
please inform us and we will gladly replace it.

Music Sales' complete catalogue describes thousands of titles
and is available in full colour sections by subject,
direct from Music Sales Limited. Please state your areas of interest
and send a cheque/postal order for £1.50 for postage to:
Music Sales Limited, Newmarket Road,
Bury St. Edmunds, Suffolk IP33 3YB.

1st Movement Themes
from Symphony No.6 (Pastoral)

Not too fast

Ludwig van Beethoven

1st Movement Theme

Eine Kleine Nachtmusik

K. 525

Bright

Wolfgang Amadeus Mozart

2nd Movement Theme
from Piano Sonata (Pathétique) Op.13

Moderately

Ludwig van Beethoven

2nd Movement Theme
from Symphony No.7

Moderately

Ludwig van Beethoven

3rd Movement Theme
from Piano Concerto No.1 in C (Rondo) Op.15

Gaily

Ludwig van Beethoven

Air
from The Peasant Cantata

Moderately

Johann Sebastian Bach

Air in D Major
from Orchestral Suite in D

Slow

Johann Sebastian Bach

Ave Verum Corpus

Slow

Wolfgang Amadeus Mozart

Badinerie
from Orchestral Suite in B minor

Bright

Johann Sebastian Bach

Bourrée

Bright

Johann Sebastian Bach

Bourrée No. 1
from Orchestral Suite in C

Johann Sebastian Bach

But Who May Abide
from Messiah

Moderately slow

George Frideric Handel

Dead March from Saul

Slow

George Frideric Handel

Elvira Madigan
Theme from Piano Concerto in C Major
K. 467

Slow

Wolfgang Amadeus Mozart

German Dance

Bright

Ludwig van Beethoven

Grand March from Aida

With breadth

Giuseppe Verdi

He Shall Feed His Flock
from Messiah

Moderately

George Frideric Handel

Hornpipe
from Water Music

Bright

George Frideric Handel

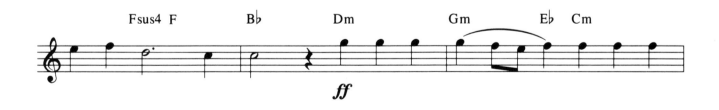

I Know That My Redeemer Liveth
from Messiah

Not too slow

George Frideric Handel

In Tears Of Grief
from St Matthew Passion

Moderately

Johann Sebastian Bach

25

Jesu, Joy Of Man's Desiring

With easy movement

Johann Sebastian Bach

Largo
from Xerxes

George Frideric Handel

Last Movement Theme
from Symphony No.9 (Ode To Joy)

With movement

Ludwig van Beethoven

Let The Bright Seraphim
from Samson

With movement

George Frideric Handel

March
from Scipione

With movement

George Frideric Handel

Military March

Bright

Franz Schubert

Minuet in G

Moderately

Johann Sebastian Bach

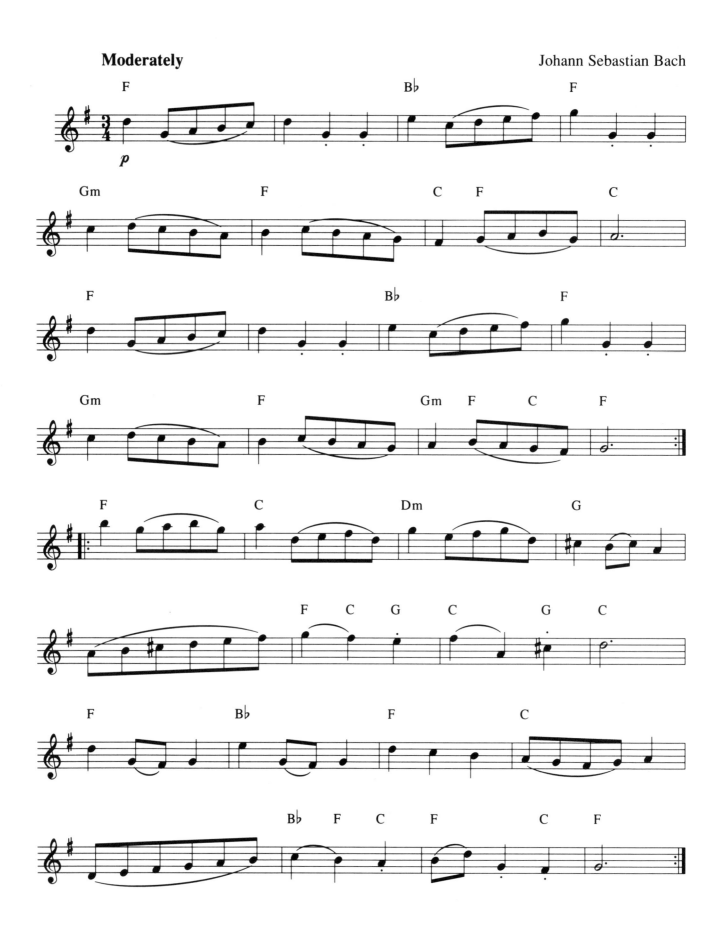

Minuet In G

Moderately

Ludwig van Beethoven

Pomp And Circumstance March No. 1

With grandeur

Sir Edward Elgar

Romance
from Eine Kleine Nachtmusik
K. 525

Slowly

Wolfgang Amadeus Mozart

Radetzky March

Johann Strauss

Rondo Alla Turca
from Sonata in A
K. 300

With movement

Wolfgang Amadeus Mozart

Plymouth District Library
Self Checkout
3/22/2014

Thank you for using self-checkout!

**********6528

33387001621483
The clarinet and clarinet playing
Date Due: 4/12/2014,23:59

33387001621186
50+ easy classical solos for clarinet [music]
Date Due: 4/12/2014,23:59

33387004004745
Noir blue [compact disc]
Date Due: 3/29/2014,23:59

33387004552461
The essential Benny Goodman [compact
disc]
Date Due: 3/29/2014,23:59

33387004552669
Pete Fountain [compact disc]
Date Due: 3/29/2014,23:59

33387004793586
Clarinet is king [compact disc] : songs of
great clarinetists
Date Due: 3/29/2014,23:59

33387004

Say Goodbye Now To Pastime
from The Marriage Of Figaro

Bright

Wolfgang Amadeus Mozart

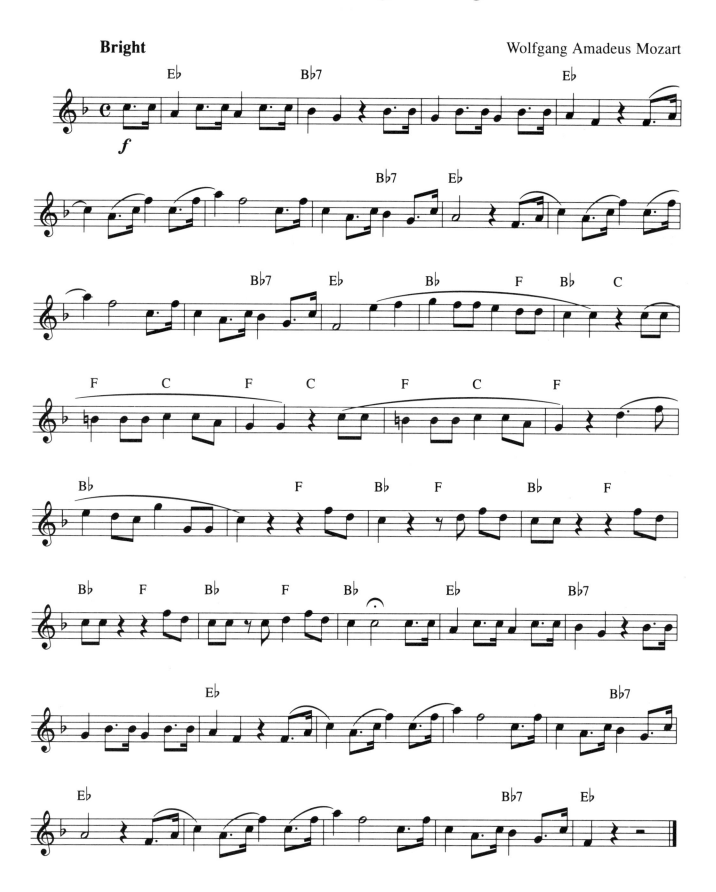

See The Conquering Hero Comes
from Judas Maccabaeus

Majestically

George Frideric Handel

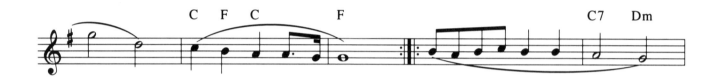

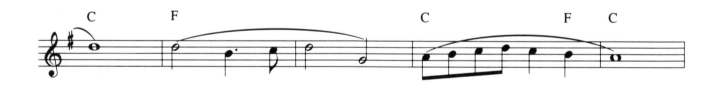

Sheep May Safely Graze

Moderately

Johann Sebastian Bach

43

Slow Movement Theme
from Symphony No.5

Moderately

Ludwig van Beethoven

Sleepers, Wake! A Voice Is Calling

Moderately

Johann Sebastian Bach

rall.

Sonata in A
1st Movement Theme
K. 300

Moderately

Wolfgang Amadeus Mozart

Sonata in C
2nd Movement Theme
K. 545

Slowly

Wolfgang Amadeus Mozart

Sonata in C Minor
Last Movement Theme
K. 456

Bright

Wolfgang Amadeus Mozart

Song: "Lullaby"

Moderately

Wolfgang Amadeus Mozart

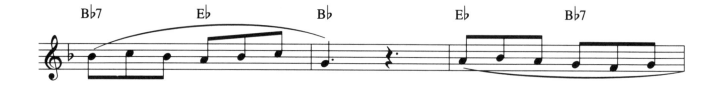

Symphony No.1 in C Minor
4th Movement Theme

Moderately

Johannes Brahms

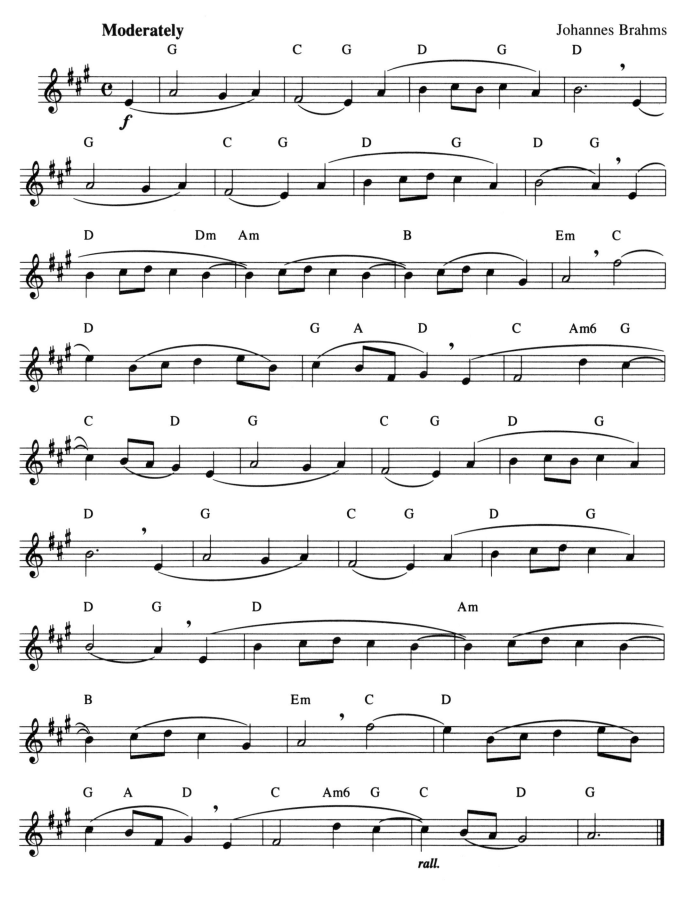

Symphony No.3 in F
3rd Movement Theme

Moderately

Johannes Brahms

Symphony No.5
Extract from Andante Cantabile

Slowly and with feeling

Peter Ilyich Tchaikovsky

Symphony No.6 (Pathétique)
1st Movement Theme

Slowly

Peter Ilyich Tchaikovsky

Symphony No.9 in E Minor
(From The New World)
2nd Movement Theme

Slowly

Antonin Dvořák

Symphony No.9 in E Minor
(From The New World)
Finale

With vigour

Antonin Dvořák

Symphony No.94 in G (Surprise)
2nd Movement Theme

Moderately

Franz Joseph Haydn

Tell Me Fair Ladies
from The Marriage Of Figaro

Moderately

Wolfgang Amadeus Mozart

Tempo di Menuetto
from Sonata in G, Op. 49, No. 2

Moderately

Ludwig van Beethoven

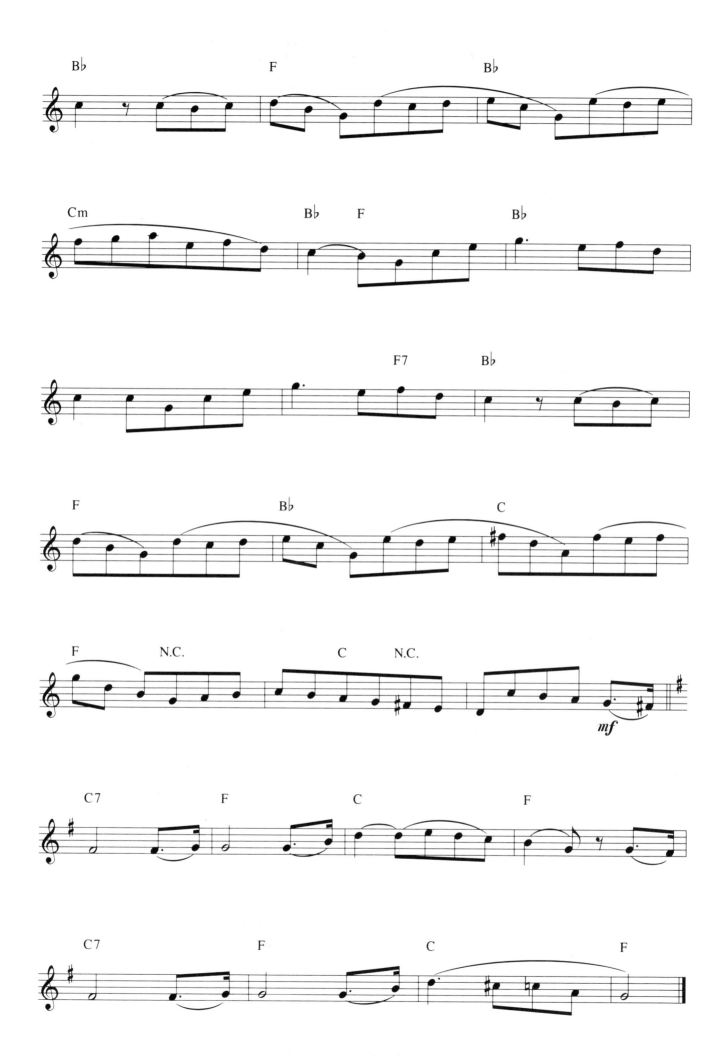

The Manly Heart That Claims Our Duty

from The Magic Flute

Moderately

Wolfgang Amadeus Mozart

Theme from Symphony in G Minor
K. 550

With movement

Wolfgang Amadeus Mozart

9/97(28754)

The Beatles

Enya

Phil Collins

Van Morrison

Bob Dylan

Sting

Paul Simon

Tracy Chapman

Eric Clapton

Pink Floyd

New Kids On The Block

Bryan Adams

Tina Turner

Elton John

Bee Gees

Whitney Houston

AC/DC

Bringing you the words

All the latest in rock and pop. Plus the brightest and best in West End show scores. Music books for every instrument under the sun. And exciting new teach-yourself ideas like "Let's Play Keyboard" - in cassette/book packs, or on video. Available from all good music shops.

and music

Music Sales' complete catalogue lists thousands of titles and is available free from your local music shop, or direct from Music Sales Limited. Please send a cheque or postal order for £1.50 (for postage) to:

Music Sales Limited
Newmarket Road,
Bury St Edmunds,
Suffolk IP33 3YB

Buddy

Five Guys Named Moe

Les Misérables

West Side Story

Phantom Of The Opera

Show Boat

The Rocky Horror Show

Bringing you the world's best music.